SUPER DOODLES

ARCTURUS

This edition published in 2012 by Arcturus Publishing Limited
26/27 Bickels Yard, 151–153 Bermondsey Street,
London SE1 3HA

ISBN: 978-1-84858-089-3
CH002532US

Illustrator: David Mostyn
Editor: Fiona Tulloch

Supplier 16, Date 0712, Print run 2064

Printed in Singapore

The King has made a fun new law!

What funny clothes your neighbors wear!

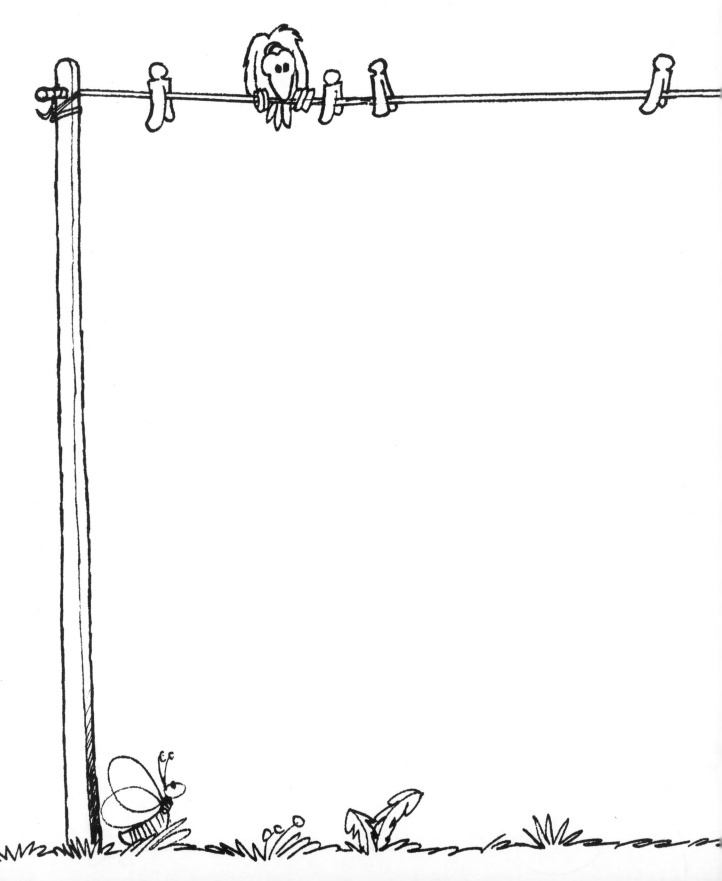

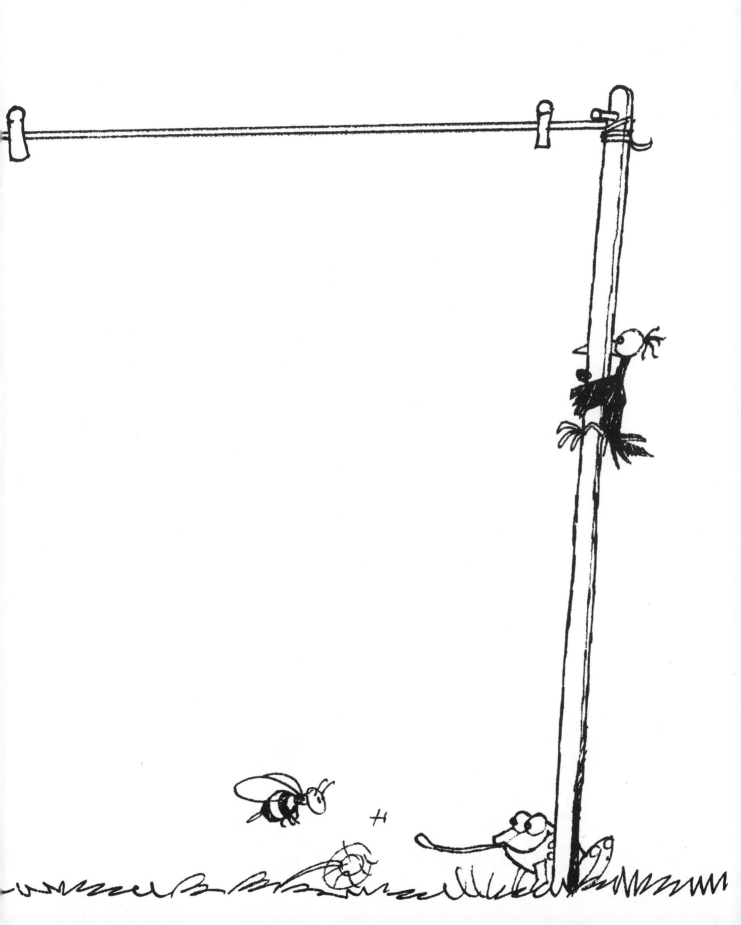

They've stolen the picnic!

What are you planning?

An Invitation

Dear . . .

You are cordially invited to . . .

From . . .

Give her a fabulous hat

Eeek! The frog didn't turn into a prince after all!!

What color are the cheerleaders' outfits?

Doodle some more go-faster karts in this race

Make the monsters feel whole again

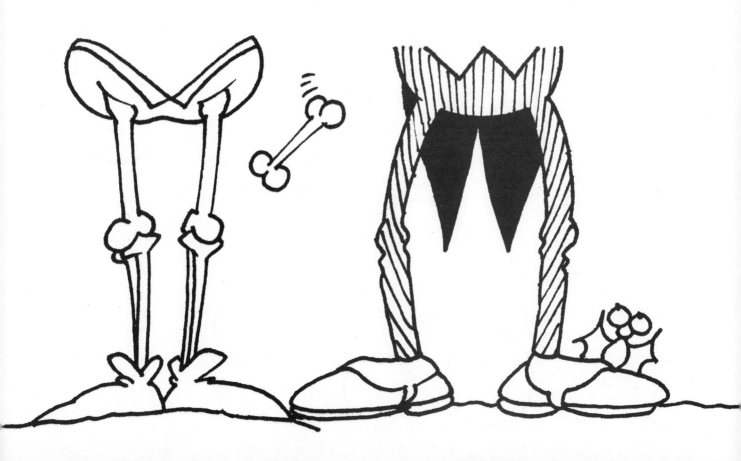

Cool marbles-all different colors!

Draw the champion alley cat

The aliens have landed!
But what colors have they
painted their spaceship?

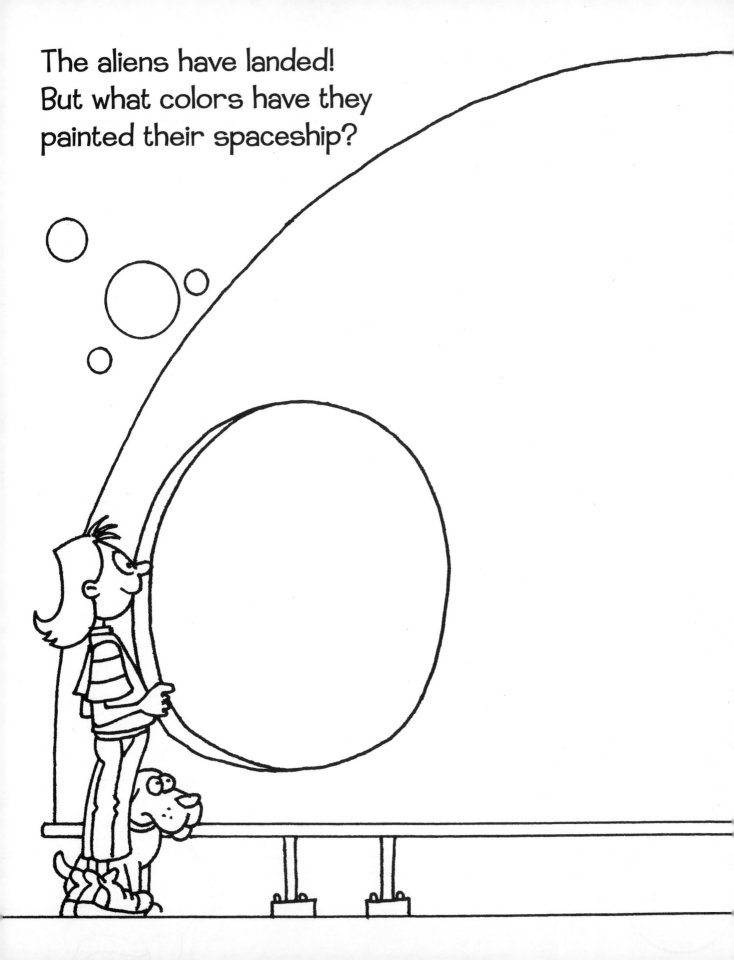

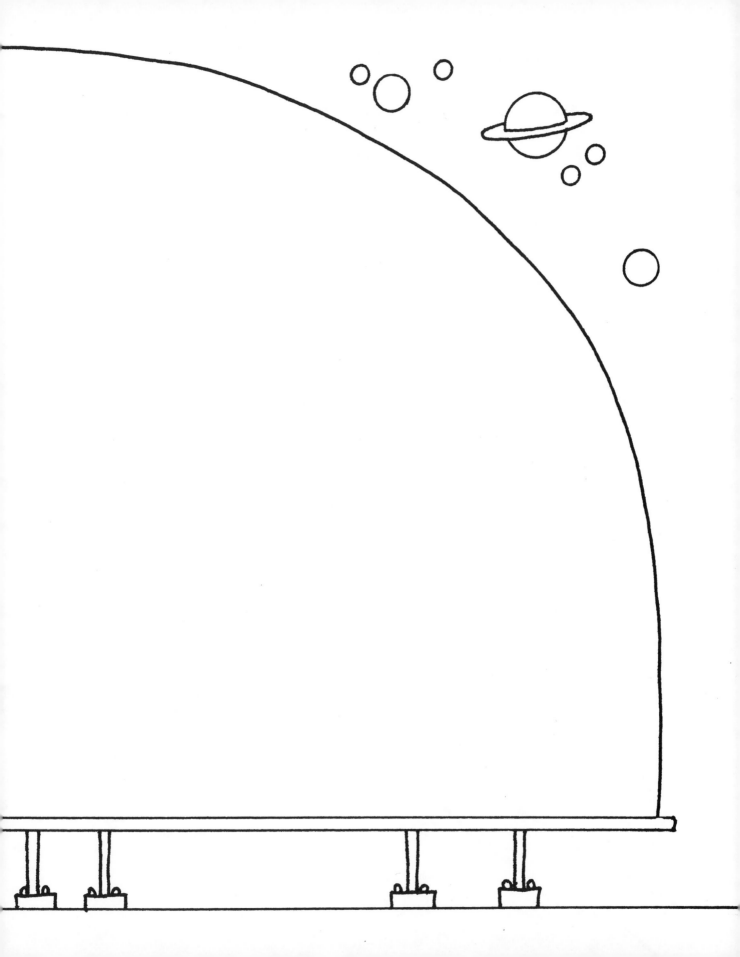

Looks like Ron's discovered something!

He's a businessman by day...

...but a superhero by night!

Who is pulling Santa's sled?

What's caused a commotion on the farm?

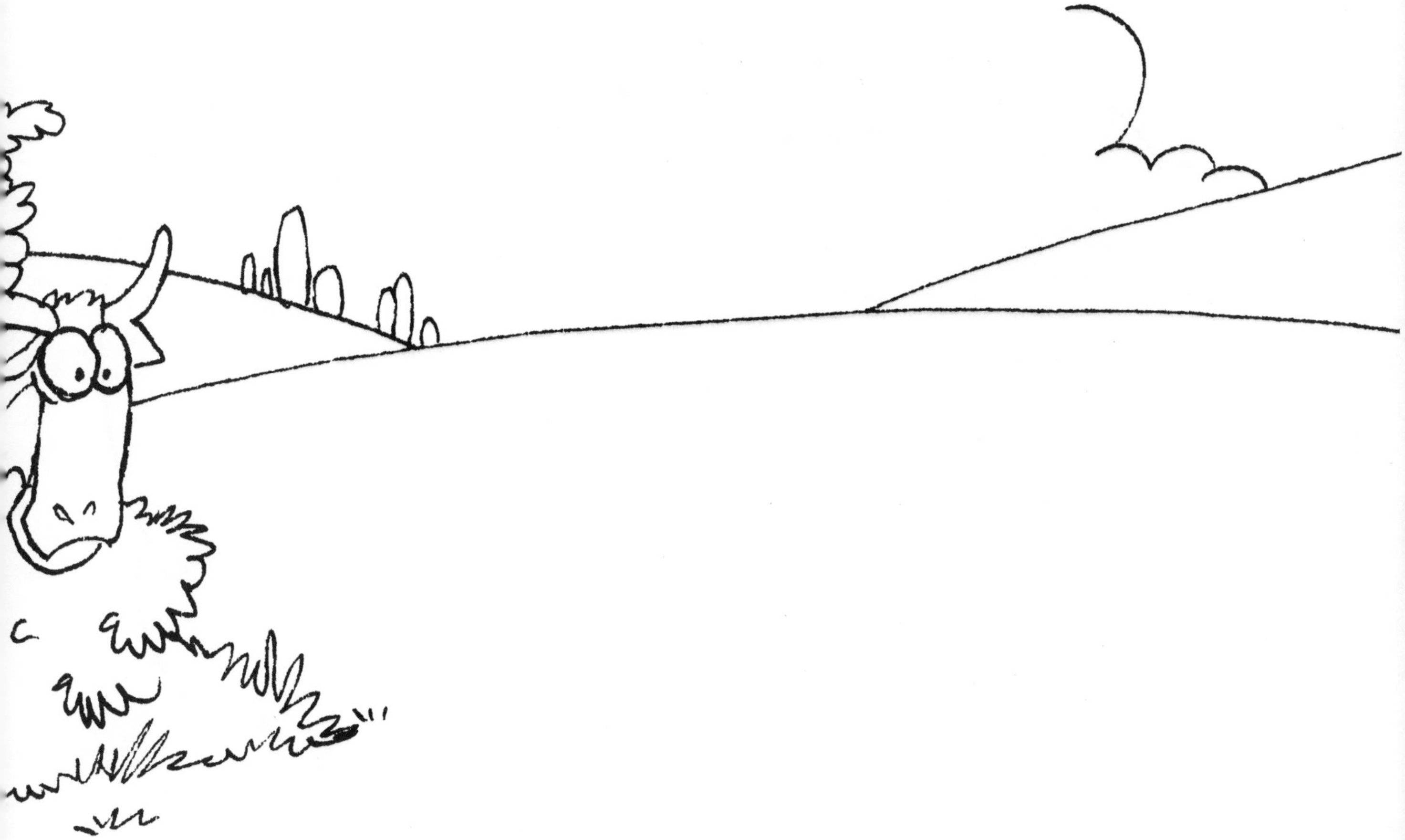

What do dogs really think?

Draw the haunted house on the hill

Doodle some more pretty night flyers

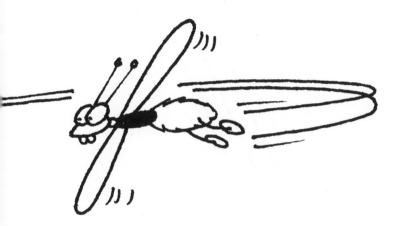

What beast is he battling with?

Liven up this boring sitting room

An ugly ducking always turns into...

...a beautiful bird!

Surprise! What's Grandpa been making all this time?

Decorate Sally's camper

A monster takeout!

What's lurking underneath your bed?

Who's wearing the wrong color team shirt?

What type of monster has this mad
scientist created?

Looks like Derek's in for a bumpy landing

This fish needs some scales

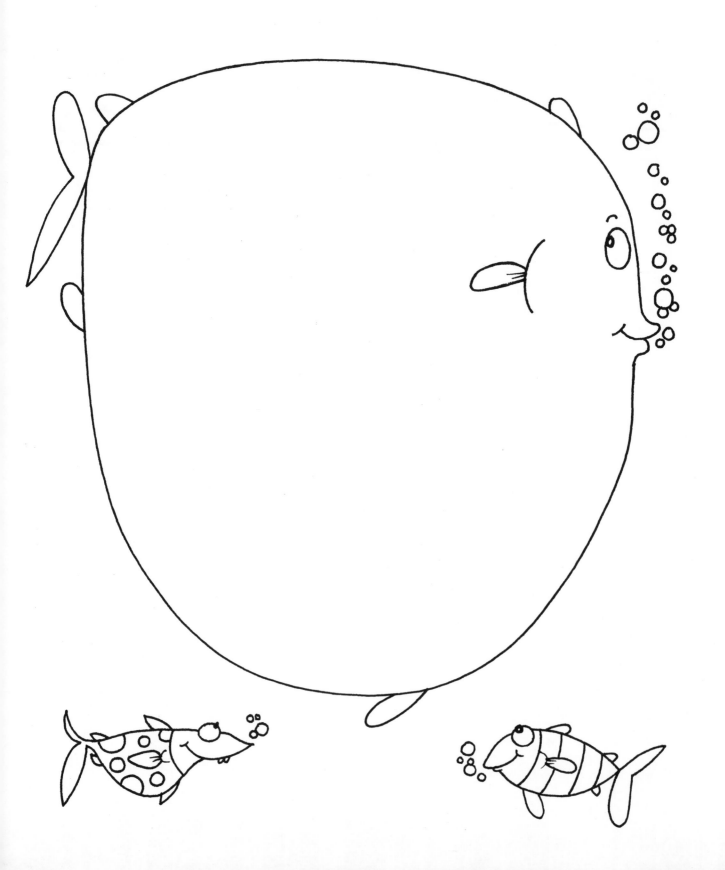

Build a brilliant treehouse

Color in Ice Man's cool set of wheels

What else is this hungry goat planning to chomp?

What are these boys up to?

Every trucker needs a truckin' hat

This fruit is all the wrong color!

What act are they watching?

Doodle the rest of the caveman's family

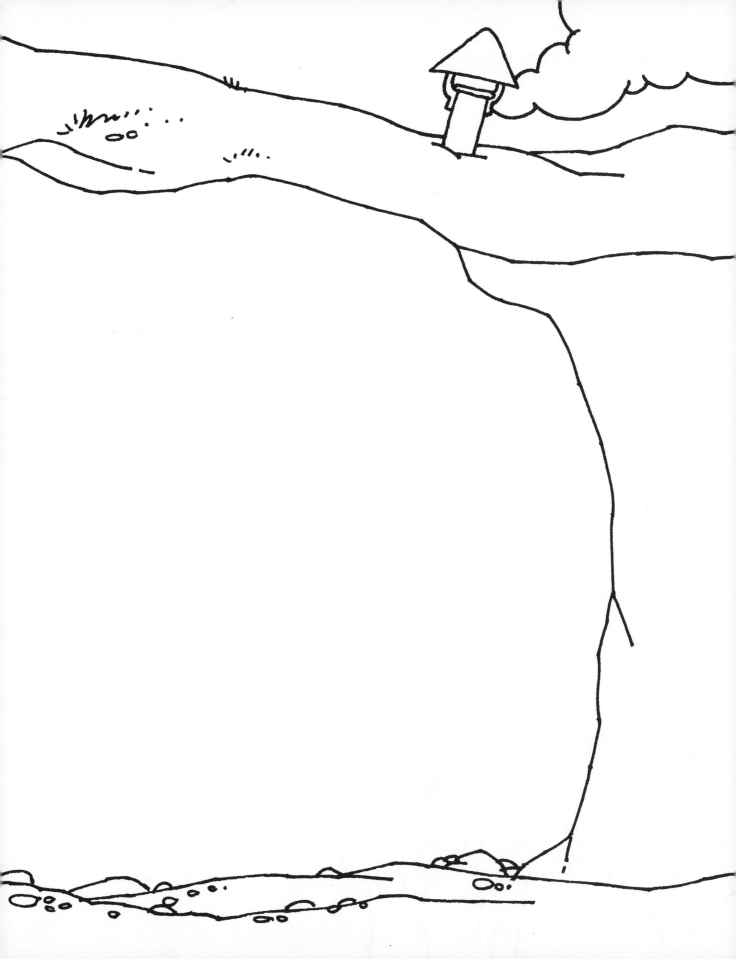

Doodle a cool pattern for Mom's new coat

What are these hyenas laughing at?

Doodle some more boats on the lake

Doodle an amazing place...

...for this magic carpet to land

Who is Ben going to share his yummy cake with?

What an excellent hiding place

What does the future hold?

Who is he saving from the burning building?

Eeew! Who made this heap of smelly dung?

I'd like to buy that car

Give the doll's house some furniture

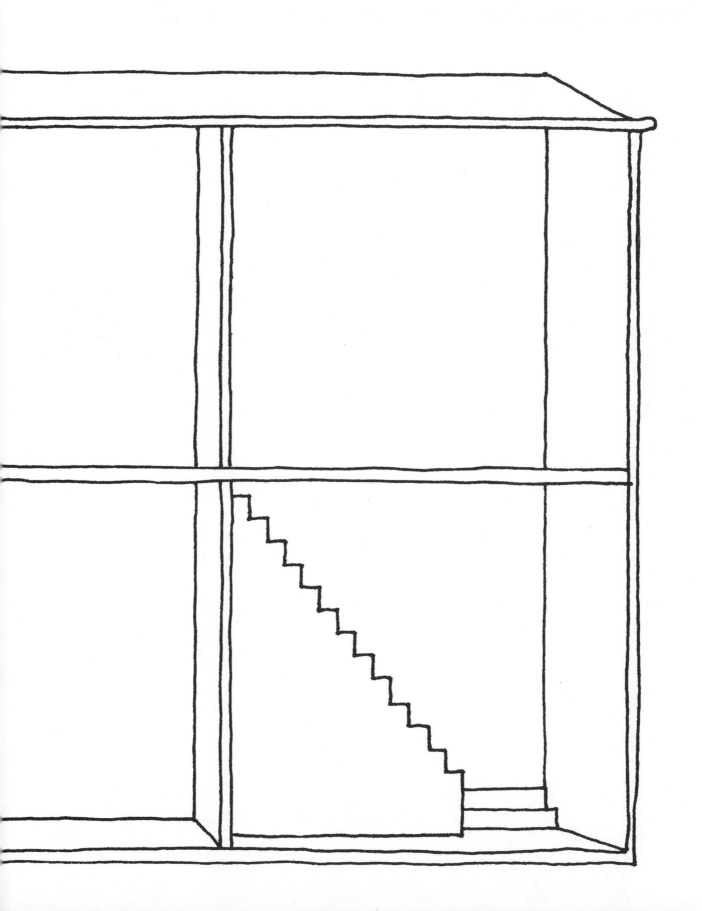

What do you see in the mirror every day?

Finish and color the pile of fall leaves

They could see their bright tents from miles away!

Fred and Lucy love playing frisbee!

Doodle some more fun beach games

He may look mean, but he's such a silly color

Ouch! What has the crab caught in his pincer?

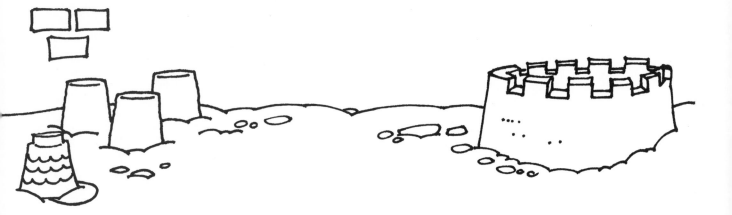

Doodle a beautiful castle for this princess

What can you see through the keyhole?

Who's flying on the magic carpet?

At last! The weary knights have reached the castle!

Doodle some naughty friends on the holiday bus!

Doodle some more cool inventions

What has this elephant just remembered?

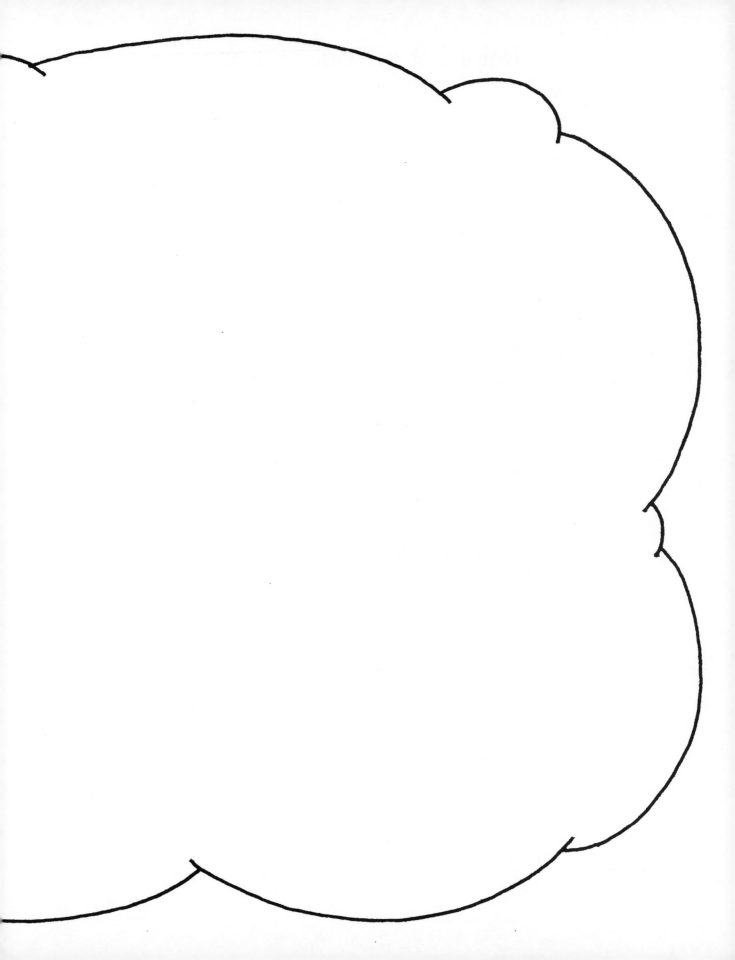

Help! Get me out of here!!

This skateboard park is painted some crazy colors!

Who's appearing at the big top tonight?

Draw the surfers who are catching this big wave

Who did Red Riding Hood meet
in the woods this time?

This ferris wheel has some really strange passengers!

Doodle the house that Jack built

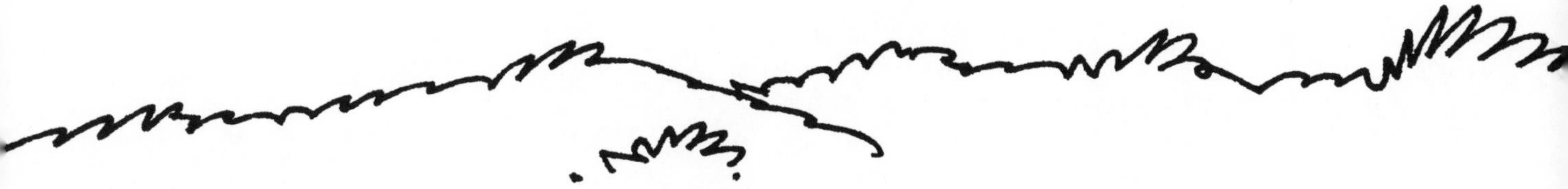

Doodle some more flying pigs!

Who else is balancing on the tightrope?

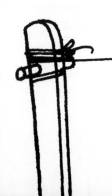

Doodle some more funny houses on this street!

Doodle two weird homes for these alien neighbors!

Fill the page with lots more superheroes!

Finish drawing the jungle for these lively monkeys

Who is Snow White's visitor?

What does Nessie keep in her lair?

Wow! This snail has a really colorful shell!

How old is Billy today?